ERIC HARVEY

# THE LEADERSHIP SECRETS of SANTA CLAUS

## WORKBOOK

*An Interactive Guide to a Productive Workshop...All Year Long!*

simple **truths**
small books. **BIG IMPACT.**

Photo Credits
Internals: page 1, Joe_Potato/Getty Images

Published by Simple Truths, an imprint of Sourcebooks, Inc.
P.O. Box 4410, Naperville, Illinois 60567-4410
(630) 961-3900
Fax: (630) 961-2168
www.sourcebooks.com

Originally published in 2003 in the United States of America by Performance Systems Corporation.

Printed and bound in the United States of America.
VP 10 9 8 7 6 5 4 3 2

# INSTRUCTIONS

Read the corresponding chapter in *The Leadership Secrets of Santa Claus* **before** beginning each section of this workbook. Then, keep the book handy to use as a reference for completing some of the material found in these pages.

# CONTENTS

# BUILD A WONDERFUL WORKSHOP

🎁 **Make the Mission the Main Thing**

🎁 **Focus on Your People As Well As Your Purpose**

🎁 **Let Values Be Your Guide**

"It seems to me that what makes a workshop wonderful is not walls and ceilings, but what happens *inside* those walls and *under* those ceilings...it's not how a workshop *stands*, but what it *stands for* that makes it special."

# ❄ Make the Mission the Main Thing

*What Santa does ...*

A) Make sure that everyone knows what the mission is and why it's important.

Our organization's "mission":

. . . . . . . . . . . . . . . . . . . . . . . . . . . . . . . . . . . . . . . . . . . . . . . . . . . . . . . . . . . . . . . . . . . .

Why it's important:

. . . . . . . . . . . . . . . . . . . . . . . . . . . . . . . . . . . . . . . . . . . . . . . . . . . . . . . . . . . . . . . . . . . .

B) Discuss with employees how their jobs link with, and contribute to, accomplishing the mission.

*Identify three employees who report to you and how their jobs link to your mission:*

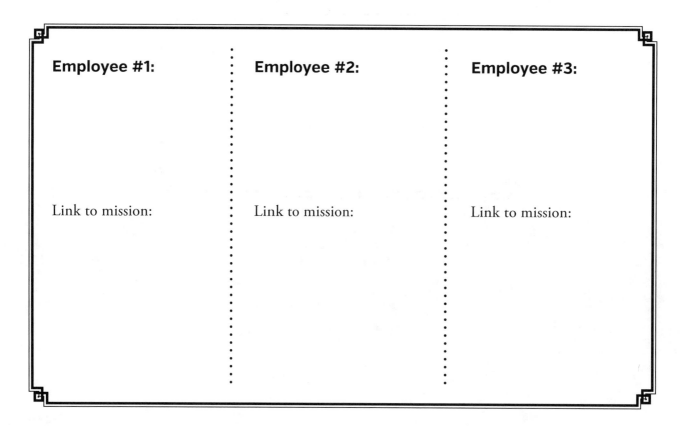

**Employee #1:**

Link to mission:

**Employee #2:**

Link to mission:

**Employee #3:**

Link to mission:

C) Keep the mission "in front of folks."

*Identify three ways you can (and will) ensure ongoing awareness of your mission:*

1 ................................................................

2 ................................................................

3 ................................................................

D) Make the mission a core component of decision-making and work planning.

| A decision I'm facing: | A project/work I need to plan: |
|---|---|
| How I will use our mission in making that decision: | How I will use our mission in planning that project: |

# ✳ Focus on Your People As Well As Your Purpose

*Identify five things you can (and will) do in the next several months to demonstrate interest in, and concern for, the people who report to you:*

1 ................................................................

2 ................................................................

3 ................................................................

4 ................................................................

5 ................................................................

# ✳ Let Values Be Your Guide

*Identify three important values of your organization or work group. Then, for each value, indicate two ways you can (and will) help the people who report to you bring that value to life:*

| Value #1: | Value #2: | Value #3: |
|---|---|---|
| Ways to bring it to life: | Ways to bring it to life: | Ways to bring it to life: |
| 1. | 1. | 1. |
| 2. | 2. | 2. |

# CHOOSE YOUR REINDEER WISELY

🎁 **Hire Tough So You Can Manage Easy**

🎁 **Promote the Right Ones...for the Right Reasons**

🎁 **Go for the Diversity Advantage**

"Because it's employees who ultimately make our mission happen, staffing is my single most important responsibility."

# ❄ Hire Tough So You Can Manage Easy

*Evaluate the last hiring activities you were involved with by placing an X on the scale:*

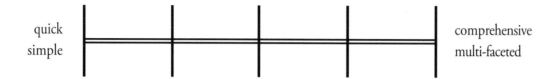

quick
simple

comprehensive
multi-faceted

*Check the activities that were included in your last hiring process. Then, circle those that you can (and will) do in the future to make sure you "hire tough":*

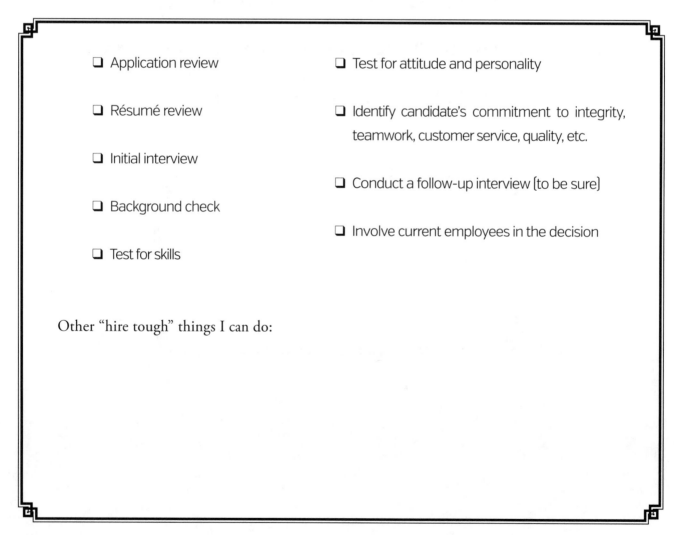

❑ Application review

❑ Résumé review

❑ Initial interview

❑ Background check

❑ Test for skills

❑ Test for attitude and personality

❑ Identify candidate's commitment to integrity, teamwork, customer service, quality, etc.

❑ Conduct a follow-up interview (to be sure)

❑ Involve current employees in the decision

Other "hire tough" things I can do:

*Note: Be sure to check with your manager, your Human Resources department, and/or your corporate headquarters before implementing these initiatives.*

# ❋ Promote the Right Ones... for the Right Reasons

*First complete the criteria for the position—the tasks, duties, and responsibilities of the position.*

*Next, complete the characteristics, talents, values, abilities, and attitudes of a successful candidate.*

*Then, connect the items in both columns with lines indicating which characteristics are directly related (and would help someone perform) the duties of the position.*

| Criteria for Position | Characteristics of a Successful Candidate |
|---|---|
| 1 ............................... | 1 ............................... |
| 2 ............................... | 2 ............................... |
| 3 ............................... | 3 ............................... |
| 4 ............................... | 4 ............................... |
| 5 ............................... | 5 ............................... |

*Finally, analyze your results. If each item in the left column doesn't connect with one or more items in the right column, you may be promoting the wrong people...for the wrong reasons.*

# ❇ Go for the Diversity Advantage

Advantages of a diverse workforce (list as many as you can think of):

*What I can (and will) do—according to our hiring and promotion policies—to help my organization realize this competitive advantage:*

1 ...................................................................................

2 ...................................................................................

3 ...................................................................................

# MAKE A LIST AND CHECK IT TWICE

🎁 **Plan Your Work**

🎁 **Work Your Plan**

🎁 **Make the Most of What You Have**

"Our success—and resulting reputation for excellence—is the result of clearly defined goals combined with well-thought-out plans to accomplish those goals."

# ✳ Plan Your Work

*Identify a work-related goal you want to accomplish, and practice planning for it by completing the following:*

**WHAT** needs to
be accomplished?   . . . . . . . . . . . . . . . . . . . . . . . . . . . . . . . . . . . . . .

**WHY** does it need to be
done? (How does it
contribute to our
overall mission?)   . . . . . . . . . . . . . . . . . . . . . . . . . . . . . . . . . . . . . .

**WHEN** does it need to
be accomplished?   . . . . . . . . . . . . . . . . . . . . . . . . . . . . . . . . . . . . . .

**WHERE** am I (are we)
now in relation to
this goal?   . . . . . . . . . . . . . . . . . . . . . . . . . . . . . . . . . . . . . .

**WHO** will be involved in
accomplishing this?   . . . . . . . . . . . . . . . . . . . . . . . . . . . . . . . . . . . . . .

**HOW** will it be done?
(What activities and steps
are involved?
What resources are required?)   . . . . . . . . . . . . . . . . . . . . . . . . . . . . . . . . . .

**WHAT** contingencies should
we plan for? (What might
unexpectedly hamper
achievement?)   . . . . . . . . . . . . . . . . . . . . . . . . . . . . . . . . . . . . . .

# ❊ Work Your Plan

*Using the frequency scale, evaluate yourself on the components for working a plan listed below:*

| USUALLY | SOMETIMES | RARELY | |
|---|---|---|---|
| ☐ | ☐ | ☐ | I make sure that others involved are informed and "on board." |
| ☐ | ☐ | ☐ | I make sure that required resources are available. |
| ☐ | ☐ | ☐ | I implement the plan as quickly as possible (with appropriate approvals). |
| ☐ | ☐ | ☐ | I keep it on (or close to) the top of my priority list. |
| ☐ | ☐ | ☐ | I regularly monitor progress (at set specific review times). |
| ☐ | ☐ | ☐ | I make "midcourse corrections" as needed. |
| ☐ | ☐ | ☐ | I periodically reevaluate the validity/relevance of the goal. |
| ☐ | ☐ | ☐ | I stay within time frames and meet deadlines. |

Now, analyze your results. Any components marked "rarely" are problem areas that need to be addressed immediately. Those marked "sometimes" represent enhancement opportunities.

# ✳ Make the Most of What You Have

### MAKING THE MOST OF **TIME**

One thing I do now that I'll **continue** to do:

One thing I don't do now that I'll **start** doing:

### MAKING THE MOST OF **MONEY**

One thing I do now that I'll **continue** to do:

One thing I don't do now that I'll **start** doing:

### MAKING THE MOST OF **MATERIALS & EQUIPMENT**

One thing I do now that I'll **continue** to do:

One thing I don't do now that I'll **start** doing:

### MAKING THE MOST OF **EMPLOYEE TALENT & EXPERTISE**

One thing I do now that I'll **continue** to do:

One thing I don't do now that I'll **start** doing:

# LISTEN TO THE ELVES

🎁 **Open Your Ears to Participation**

🎁 **Pay Attention to How You're Perceived**

🎁 **Walk Awhile in *Their* Shoes**

"Now I ask for (and listen to) the elves' ideas and opinions on most everything we do. I even let *them* make many of the toy-making decisions we face. And the production line has never run better."

# ✳ Open Your Ears to Participation

Various ways that employees can participate (get involved) in the running of any business:

Advantages (benefits) of employee participation:

*Identify two obstacles of employee participation and how you can try to overcome them:*

**Obstacle:**....................

........................

........................

........................

**Solution:**....................

........................

........................

........................

**Obstacle:**....................

........................

........................

........................

**Solution:**....................

........................

........................

........................

Things I'm working on now—and things coming up—that I will use as opportunities for employee involvement:

# ✳ Pay Attention to How You're Perceived

*Respond to each statement listed below:*

| YES | NO | |
|-----|-----|-----|
| ☐ | ☐ | I conduct periodic surveys to see what employees think of our leadership. |
| ☐ | ☐ | I regularly ask the people who report to me to assess how I'm doing. |
| ☐ | ☐ | I've told my employees that I'm interested in their feedback. |
| ☐ | ☐ | I frequently end meetings and coaching sessions by asking employees to rate *ME*. |
| ☐ | ☐ | I've established ways that employees can give me feedback anonymously. |
| ☐ | ☐ | I've received "360° feedback" on my leadership performance within the last year. |
| ☐ | ☐ | I use employee performance as a gauge of my leadership skills. |
| ☐ | ☐ | I've talked with my boss, other managers, and HR to identify things I can do to get feedback from my people on how I fare as a leader. |

Now, review your results. Those items marked with a "no" represent possible ways for you to find out what your people think of your leadership performance. Implement as many of them as you can!

*What two key requirements for making the feedback process work
did Santa receive via the employee hotline?*

1. . . . . . . . . . . . . . . . . . . . . . . . . . . . . . . . . . . . . . . . . . . . . . . . . . . . . . . . . . . . . . . . . . .

2. . . . . . . . . . . . . . . . . . . . . . . . . . . . . . . . . . . . . . . . . . . . . . . . . . . . . . . . . . . . . . . . . .

## ❊ **Walk Awhile in *Their* Shoes**

*Identify four things that YOUR boss could do to demonstrate empathy for YOU
(to walk awhile in YOUR shoes):*

1. . . . . . . . . . . . . . . . . . . . . . . . . . . . . . . . . . . . . . . . . . . . . . . . . . . . . . . . . . . . . . . .

2. . . . . . . . . . . . . . . . . . . . . . . . . . . . . . . . . . . . . . . . . . . . . . . . . . . . . . . . . . . . . . . .

3. . . . . . . . . . . . . . . . . . . . . . . . . . . . . . . . . . . . . . . . . . . . . . . . . . . . . . . . . . . . . . . .

4. . . . . . . . . . . . . . . . . . . . . . . . . . . . . . . . . . . . . . . . . . . . . . . . . . . . . . . . . . . . . . . .

*Now, go back and circle those items that you regularly do with, and for,
YOUR employees. Are there one or more that you didn't circle? Make a
personal commitment to start doing it/them today.*

# SAY HO HO HO,
# BUT DON'T FORGET THE SNOW

🎁 **Build Contagious Enthusiasm**

🎁 **Expect the Unexpected**

🎁 **Get Problems Solved...Together**

"To truly build a workshop that is filled with positive energy, I not only need to set the example individually, but also need to make the goal of recognizing positive performance part of *every* reindeer and elf's job expectations."

# ❄ Build Contagious Enthusiasm

What are some of the inexpensive yet effective things you can
do to build contagious enthusiasm in your workshop?

Describe a recognition event that happened to you and how it
made you feel:

*How well do you follow Santa's rules for effective recognition?*

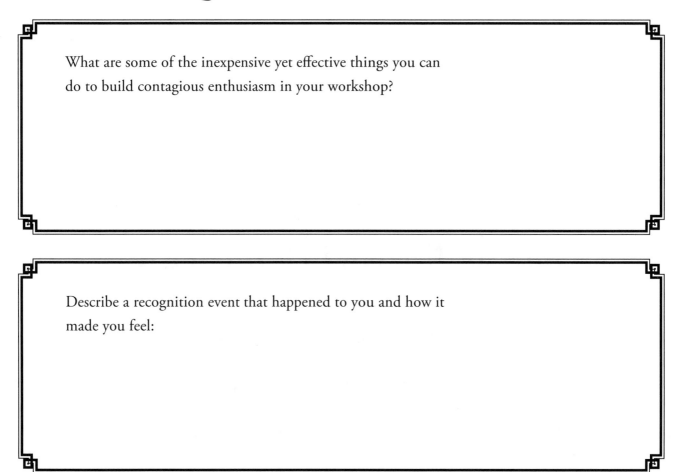

|  |  |  |  |
|---|---|---|---|
| USUALLY | SOMETIMES | RARELY |  |
| ☐ | ☐ | ☐ | **Make it timely.** Give recognition as soon as possible. |
| ☐ | ☐ | ☐ | **Get specific.** Tell recipients exactly what they did that was positive. |
| ☐ | ☐ | ☐ | **Be appreciative.** Tell team members what the positive performance means to you. |
| ☐ | ☐ | ☐ | **Get personal.** Adjust the style and method of your recognition to the receiver. |
| ☐ | ☐ | ☐ | **Make it proportional.** Match the type and amount of recognition with the value and impact of the achievement. |

# ✳ Expect the Unexpected

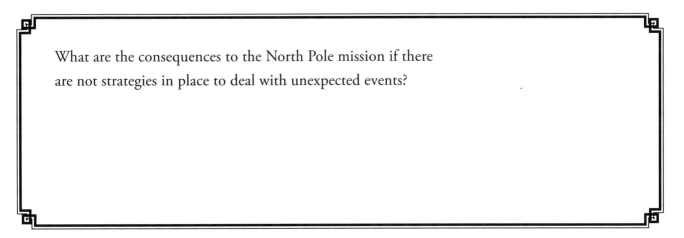

What are the consequences to the North Pole mission if there are not strategies in place to deal with unexpected events?

*Santa has a bunch of signs around the workshop to remind elves and reindeer what attitudes they need to have when unexpected events occur. Add a few more signs you might recommend:*

\*If it was easy, anyone could do it!

\*Problems are opportunities in disguise!

\* . . . . . . . . . . . . . . . . . . . . . . . . . . . . . . . . . . . . . . . . . . . . . . . . . . . . . . . . . . . . . . . . . . . . . . . . . .

\* . . . . . . . . . . . . . . . . . . . . . . . . . . . . . . . . . . . . . . . . . . . . . . . . . . . . . . . . . . . . . . . . . . . . . . . . . .

\* . . . . . . . . . . . . . . . . . . . . . . . . . . . . . . . . . . . . . . . . . . . . . . . . . . . . . . . . . . . . . . . . . . . . . . . . . .

\* . . . . . . . . . . . . . . . . . . . . . . . . . . . . . . . . . . . . . . . . . . . . . . . . . . . . . . . . . . . . . . . . . . . . . . . . . .

\* . . . . . . . . . . . . . . . . . . . . . . . . . . . . . . . . . . . . . . . . . . . . . . . . . . . . . . . . . . . . . . . . . . . . . . . . . .

# ✳ Get Problems Solved...Together

*What are some of the most effective strategies you can use to work with your team members to solve workshop problems together?*

....................................................................

....................................................................

....................................................................

....................................................................

....................................................................

....................................................................

....................................................................

....................................................................

....................................................................

....................................................................

....................................................................

....................................................................

....................................................................

....................................................................

# GIVE THEM GIFTS
# THAT LAST A LIFETIME

🎁 **Teach Success Skills**

🎁 **Reinforce Relationships**

🎁 **Push Pride and Professionalism**

"Developing a team is about more than just teaching folks how to do their jobs; it's also about teaching them how to be *successful*."

# ❋ Teach Success Skills

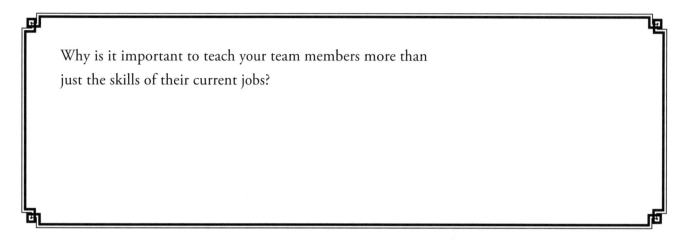

Why is it important to teach your team members more than
just the skills of their current jobs?

*List some ways you can teach your team members success skills:*

\*In new employee training

\*At staff meetings

\* . . . . . . . . . . . . . . . . . . . . . . . . . . . . . . . . . . . . . . . . . . . . . . . . . . . . . . . . . . . . . . . . . . . . . . .

\* . . . . . . . . . . . . . . . . . . . . . . . . . . . . . . . . . . . . . . . . . . . . . . . . . . . . . . . . . . . . . . . . . . . . . . .

\* . . . . . . . . . . . . . . . . . . . . . . . . . . . . . . . . . . . . . . . . . . . . . . . . . . . . . . . . . . . . . . . . . . . . . . .

\* . . . . . . . . . . . . . . . . . . . . . . . . . . . . . . . . . . . . . . . . . . . . . . . . . . . . . . . . . . . . . . . . . . . . . . .

\* . . . . . . . . . . . . . . . . . . . . . . . . . . . . . . . . . . . . . . . . . . . . . . . . . . . . . . . . . . . . . . . . . . . . . . .

# ❋ Reinforce Relationships

Why is it important to reinforce positive relationships when dealing with workshop conflicts?

*How well do you follow Santa's recommended ways to manage and resolve workshop problems?*

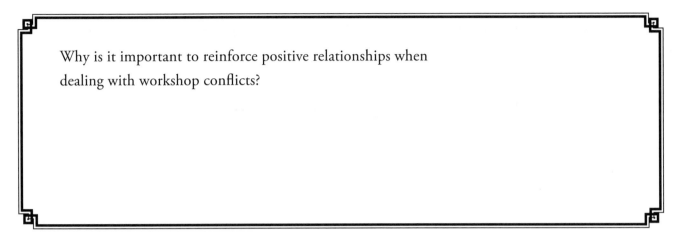

USUALLY    SOMETIMES    RARELY

☐ ☐ ☐     Agree that a problem exists.

☐ ☐ ☐     Identify each other's concerns and needs.

☐ ☐ ☐     Explore possible win-win solutions.

☐ ☐ ☐     Focus on what's right, NOT who's right.

☐ ☐ ☐     Agree on a course of action.

☐ ☐ ☐     Determine how missteps will be handled.

☐ ☐ ☐     Close on a positive note.

## ✳ Push Pride and Professionalism

*Come up with some words that signify PRIDE using the letters P, R, I, D, and E*

**P**................................

**R**................................

**I** ................................

**D**................................

**E**................................

How are you and others motivated when you feel pride in
your work and the people you work with?

# GET BEYOND THE RED WAGONS

🎁 **Help Everyone Accept the Reality of Change**

🎁 **Remember: The Customer Is Really in Charge**

🎁 **Teach "the Business" of the Business**

> "I knew we had to abandon the status quo. And as the leader, I had to make it happen with both decisiveness and sensitivity... I made sure that everyone on the team understood that change was inevitable—we had no choice whether or not it would come. Our only choice was how we responded to it."

# ❄ Help Everyone Accept the Reality of Change

Why do people tend to resist change?

*Identify four things that Santa did to help the elves deal with the red-wagon changes:*

1. . . . . . . . . . . . . . . . . . . . . . . . . . . . . . . . . . . . . . . . . . . . . . . . . . . . . . . . . . . . . . . . . . . . . . . .

2. . . . . . . . . . . . . . . . . . . . . . . . . . . . . . . . . . . . . . . . . . . . . . . . . . . . . . . . . . . . . . . . . . . . . . . .

3. . . . . . . . . . . . . . . . . . . . . . . . . . . . . . . . . . . . . . . . . . . . . . . . . . . . . . . . . . . . . . . . . . . . . . . .

4. . . . . . . . . . . . . . . . . . . . . . . . . . . . . . . . . . . . . . . . . . . . . . . . . . . . . . . . . . . . . . . . . . . . . . . .

*Identify three changes you and your people are facing at work, and which of Santa's strategies (listed above) are appropriate for you to apply in facilitating those changes:*

**Changes You Are Facing:**                     **Applicable Santa Strategies:**

1. . . . . . . . . . . . . . . . . . . . . . . . . . . . . . .        [#] [#] [#] [#]

2. . . . . . . . . . . . . . . . . . . . . . . . . . . . . . .        [#] [#] [#] [#]

3. . . . . . . . . . . . . . . . . . . . . . . . . . . . . . .        [#] [#] [#] [#]

# ❋ Remember: The Customer Is Really in Charge

*List four significant changes that have occurred in your business (or industry) in the last two years:*

❑ 1 ..............................................................................................................

❑ 2 ..............................................................................................................

❑ 3 ..............................................................................................................

❑ 4 ..............................................................................................................

*Now, go back and check the boxes of those that were the result of changing customers needs and requirements, or, an effort to attract and keep more customers.*

*What percentage (approximate) of the above changes were customer-driven? ........%*

Why it's important to stay connected to
customers and monitor competitors:

*Santa used virtual and actual field trips to keep the elves and reindeer aware of customer desires, marketplace changes, and competitor activities. How does your workforce stay connected with your consumer base? What additional things can you implement?*

Current strategies:

Two new ideas I can (and will) implement:

1.

2.

# ❄ Teach "the Business" of the Business

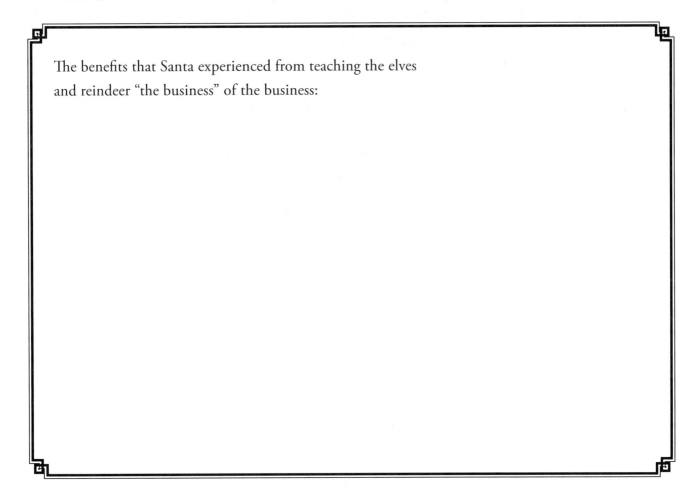

The benefits that Santa experienced from teaching the elves
and reindeer "the business" of the business:

*On average, how well-versed are your employees on basic business principles?*

little, if any,
knowledge

very
knowledgeable

*Listed below are the strategies that Santa applied to help his employees better understand their business operation. Place a check mark next to the ones that you can (and will) implement within your work group. Then, add additional initiatives that you will try in the box provided:*

☐ Asked the training staff to develop and conduct a basic business literacy course.

☐ "Opened up the books"—giving employees access to financial information such as production costs, overhead expenses, etc.

☐ Taught employees how to read and interpret the financial information and how to use it in the performance of their jobs.

☐ Had employees attend, observe, and participate in nonconfidential senior-staff meetings.

☐ Provided cross-training and rotational assignments within departments.

☐ Created departmental "swap" program so employees could see how other units operate.

Additional initiatives I can (and will) try:

# SHARE THE MILK AND COOKIES

🎁 **Help Them See the Difference They Make**

🎁 **Do Right by Those Who Do Right**

🎁 **Expand the Reinforcement Possibilities**

"Most of the elves and reindeer don't get to see and experience the same things that I do. So their feelings of satisfaction and accomplishment must come in different ways—from other sources. As the leader, I play a critical role in making that a reality."

# ❊ Help Them See the Difference They Make

*In the last six months, how have employees that report to you made a positive difference for...*

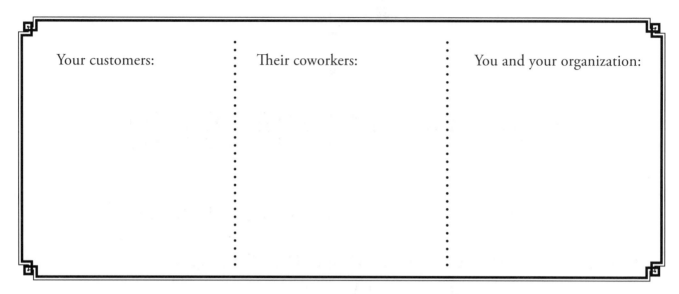

Your customers:

Their coworkers:

You and your organization:

*On average, how aware are your employees of the above differences they've made?*

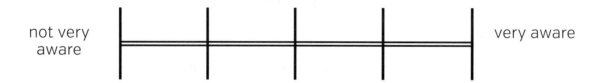

not very aware

very aware

What I can (and will) do to increase employee awareness of the positive differences they make (feel free to include the strategies employed by Santa Claus):

# ❋ Do Right by Those Who Do Right

The benefits (positive outcomes) of recognizing employees and their contributions:

*Using the frequency scale below, assess your recognition thoughts, habits, and behaviors:*

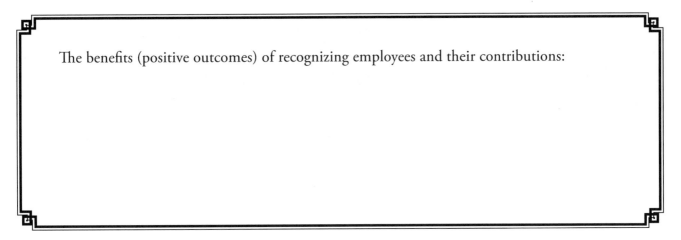

USUALLY   SOMETIMES   RARELY

☐ ☐ ☐   I look for opportunities to "catch people doing right" and recognize them for it.

☐ ☐ ☐   I give recognition to employees who perform consistently well over time.

☐ ☐ ☐   I recognize employees who have exemplary attendance for six months or more.

☐ ☐ ☐   I reward employees who go "above and beyond the call of duty."

☐ ☐ ☐   I recognize and thank employees who consistently meet my expectations.

☐ ☐ ☐   I commend employees who perform with ethics and integrity.

☐ ☐ ☐   I provide recognition to employees who support our mission and values.

☐ ☐ ☐   I appreciate employees who do good work...and I show it.

*Now, analyze your results. Any statements marked "rarely" are problem areas that you should work on changing immediately. Those marked "sometimes" represent enhancement opportunities.*

# ❊ Expand the Reinforcement Possibilities

*In the box below, list the things that Santa came up with to expand the reinforcement possibilities in his workshop. Circle those that you can (and will) do. Then identify additional nontraditional things you will do within the next one to two months to recognize your people:*

What Santa came up with:

Additional things I'll do in the next couple of months:

# FIND OUT WHO'S NAUGHTY AND NICE

🎁 **Confront Performance Problems...Early**

🎁 **Coach "the Majority in the Middle"**

🎁 **Don't Forget "the Super Stars"**

"I've come to define coaching very simply: helping the elves and reindeer avoid problems and do the best work that they can."

# ❄ Confront Performance Problems...Early

*Identify the four mistakes that Santa made with Igor the Elf:*

**Mistake #1** . . . . . . . . . . . . . . . . . . . . . . . . . . . . . . . . . . . . . . . . . . . . . . . .

**Mistake #2** . . . . . . . . . . . . . . . . . . . . . . . . . . . . . . . . . . . . . . . . . . . . . . . .

**Mistake #3** . . . . . . . . . . . . . . . . . . . . . . . . . . . . . . . . . . . . . . . . . . . . . . . .

**Mistake #4** . . . . . . . . . . . . . . . . . . . . . . . . . . . . . . . . . . . . . . . . . . . . . . . .

*Now, go back and circle the number(s) of any of the above mistakes that you have made in the past. (If you circle one or more, congratulations... you're human!)*

Next, list the negative outcomes (what happened) resulting from your mistakes:

Finally, identify what you can (and will) do to avoid committing those mistakes again in the future:

# ❄ Coach "the Majority in the Middle"

Why it's important to pay attention to/coach "middle stars":

*Listed below are the strategies that Santa applied to manage the performance of his middle stars. Review each Santa strategy and indicate if it's something you already do, something that you'll start doing, or something that's not applicable within your work group:*

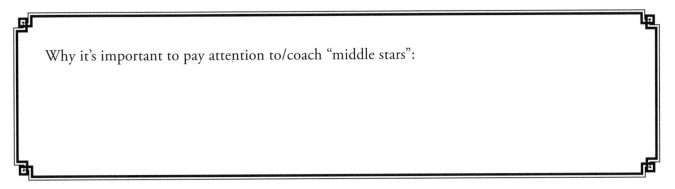

| ALREADY DO IT | WILL START DOING IT | N/A | |
|---|---|---|---|
| ☐ | ☐ | ☐ | Make sure that they know and understand the performance expectations that come with their jobs. |
| ☐ | ☐ | ☐ | Provide the training and resources they need to meet those expectations. |
| ☐ | ☐ | ☐ | Give frequent and specific feedback on how they're doing. |
| ☐ | ☐ | ☐ | Identify any obstacles they may be facing and do my best to eliminate those barriers. |
| ☐ | ☐ | ☐ | Teach them how to set, manage, and achieve goals. |
| ☐ | ☐ | ☐ | Help them learn from mistakes...and successes. |
| ☐ | ☐ | ☐ | Hook them up with mentors from the superstar ranks. |
| ☐ | ☐ | ☐ | Stay aware of what they're doing and "nip in the bud" any problems that start to surface. |

Additional things I can (and will) try:

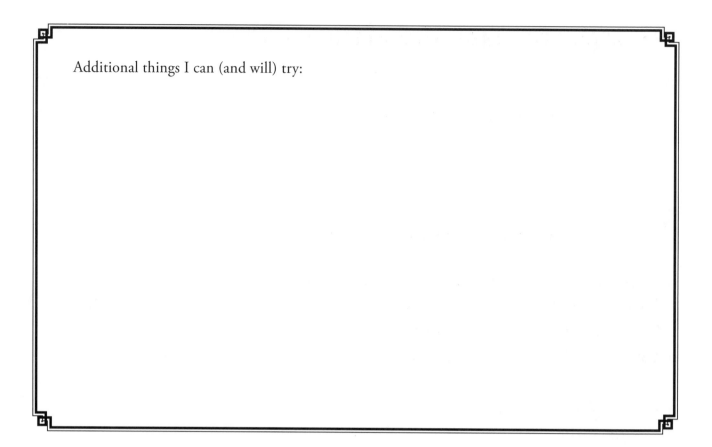

## ✳ Don't Forget "the Super Stars"

Why it can be easy to neglect/overlook your super stars:

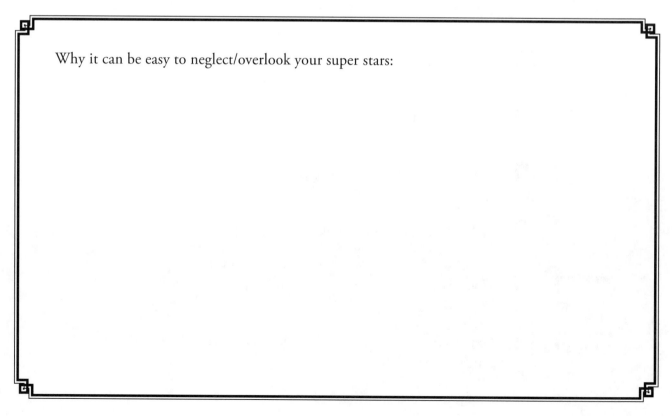

*The three coaching roles that Santa took with his super stars were:*

1 ...........................................................................

2 ...........................................................................

3 ...........................................................................

*Listed below are the strategies that Santa applied to help keep the super stars super. Review each Santa strategy and indicate if it's something you already do, something that you'll start doing, or something that's not applicable within your work group:*

ALREADY DO IT   WILL START DOING IT   N/A

☐ ☐ ☐   Get them involved in decision-making, strategy setting, procedure development, and problem solving.

☐ ☐ ☐   Delegate extensively and avoid "micromanaging" them.

☐ ☐ ☐   Encourage them to teach and mentor others...including you.

☐ ☐ ☐   Celebrate their accomplishments and successes.

☐ ☐ ☐   Provide them with highly-specialized training and other career-growth opportunities.

☐ ☐ ☐   Show interest in their work...and their lives away from work.

☐ ☐ ☐   Hold their coworkers accountable for doing their jobs so that the super stars don't have to pick up the slack.

☐ ☐ ☐   Avoid punishing them for good performance.

Additional things I can (and will) try:

# BE GOOD FOR GOODNESS SAKE

🎁 **Set the Example**

🎁 **Establish Guidelines and Accountability**

🎁 **Remember That Everything Counts**

> "Our excellent reputation—built over centuries of hard work and attention to detail—could be tarnished (or destroyed entirely) by a single inappropriate act."

# ❄ Set the Example

*Complete column one below–indicating whether or not each of the behavioral statements is an expectation that you have of your employees. BE HONEST! If you really expect it, mark "yes."*

*Then, complete column two–indicating whether or not each behavioral statement is something you practice yourself. BE HONEST! If you really don't do it, mark "no."*

*Finally, review your results. Anything marked "no" in column one suggests that your employee expectations may be too low for that behavior. Any behavior marked "no" in column two is an area for you to work on and improve. Find any marked "yes" in column one and "no" in column two? Those are problems that need to be corrected immediately!*

| I expect this from my employees | | | I do this myself | |
|---|---|---|---|---|
| **Y** | **N** | | **Y** | **N** |
| ☐ | ☐ | Follow ALL of our rules and procedures. | ☐ | ☐ |
| ☐ | ☐ | Treat EVERYONE with dignity and respect. | ☐ | ☐ |
| ☐ | ☐ | ALWAYS tell the truth. | ☐ | ☐ |
| ☐ | ☐ | NEVER break a promise or commitment. | ☐ | ☐ |
| ☐ | ☐ | Build superior quality into EVERYTHING I do. | ☐ | ☐ |
| ☐ | ☐ | CONTINUALLY give my best effort. | ☐ | ☐ |
| ☐ | ☐ | CONSISTENTLY take a stand for what's right. | ☐ | ☐ |
| 1 | | | 2 | |

*Imagine that you're about to receive your performance review from your boss. You're instructed to come to the session with a list of four examples of how you have "led by example" in the last six months. What behaviors/actions would you cite?*

1 . . . . . . . . . . . . . . . . . . . . . . . . . . . . . . . . . . . . . . . . . . . . . . . . . . . . . . . . . . . . . . . . . .

2 . . . . . . . . . . . . . . . . . . . . . . . . . . . . . . . . . . . . . . . . . . . . . . . . . . . . . . . . . . . . . . . . . .

3 . . . . . . . . . . . . . . . . . . . . . . . . . . . . . . . . . . . . . . . . . . . . . . . . . . . . . . . . . . . . . . . . . .

4 . . . . . . . . . . . . . . . . . . . . . . . . . . . . . . . . . . . . . . . . . . . . . . . . . . . . . . . . . . . . . . . . .

# ✳ Establish Guidelines and Accountability

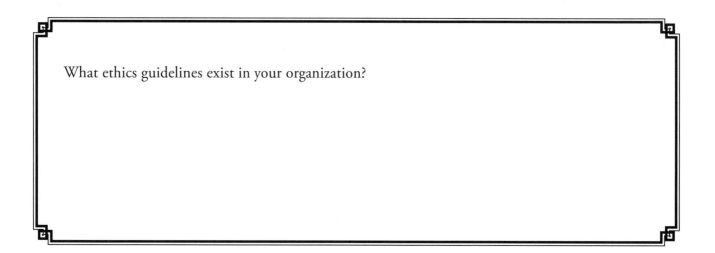

What ethics guidelines exist in your organization?

*How can you ensure that employees stay familiar with those guidelines?*

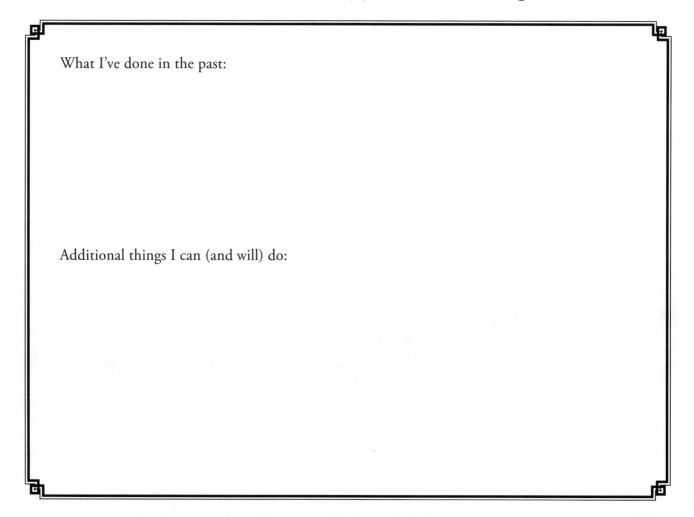

What I've done in the past:

Additional things I can (and will) do:

*Identify the three things that Santa did to build accountability for proper behavior. Under each item, place an X on the scales to rate its level of importance and your level of performance in that area:*

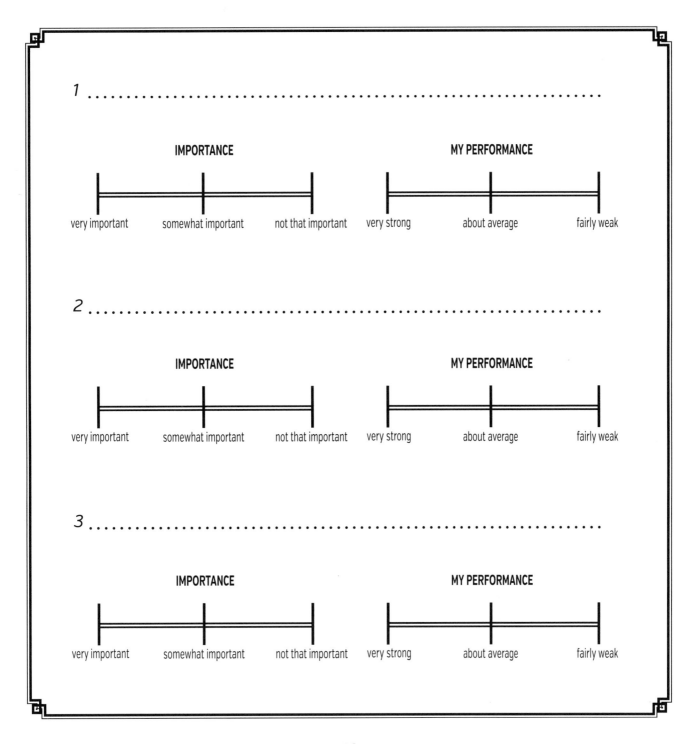

1 ................................................................

IMPORTANCE

very important    somewhat important    not that important

MY PERFORMANCE

very strong    about average    fairly weak

2 ................................................................

IMPORTANCE

very important    somewhat important    not that important

MY PERFORMANCE

very strong    about average    fairly weak

3 ................................................................

IMPORTANCE

very important    somewhat important    not that important

MY PERFORMANCE

very strong    about average    fairly weak

# ❋ Remember That Everything Counts

When it comes to ethics and integrity, what are the dangers of believing that some behaviors really don't matter that much?

*Santa learned that it was the seemingly insignificant actions and behaviors—the "small stuff"—that were the real test of his workshop's integrity. On the lines below, list as many "small" behavioral criteria as you can think of for evaluating your workplace's ethical make-up. You'll find three to get you started.*

*We can tell just how ethical we are by looking at...*

* The way we treat and talk about each other;

* The type of jokes we share;

* The little white lies we don't (or do) tell;

* .......................................................................................
.......................................................................................

* .......................................................................................
.......................................................................................

* .......................................................................................
.......................................................................................

* .......................................................................................
.......................................................................................

* .......................................................................................
.......................................................................................

* .......................................................................................
.......................................................................................

* .......................................................................................
.......................................................................................

* .......................................................................................
.......................................................................................

* .......................................................................................
.......................................................................................

# LEADERSHIP ACTION ITEMS

*Once you've completed this workbook, go back and review all of the responses and answers that you wrote down. Pay special attention to the areas you need to improve in and the things you said you can (and will) do to become a more effective leader. Those are your "action items."*

*Then, select the top three to five action items that you believe will have the greatest positive impact on your people, your organization, and your effectiveness as a leader. Describe these goals in detail on the lines below.*

*Next, make a copy of these completed pages—as a reminder—and put it in your day planner, post it on your wall, etc. Finally, start working on your items...and check your progress frequently.*

..................................................................................

..................................................................................

..................................................................................

..................................................................................

..................................................................................

..................................................................................

..................................................................................

..................................................................................

..................................................................................

# WORDS TO LEAD BY

*People need me—they depend on me. We're doing something important here. And knowing that gives me the energy to carry the sack, lead the pack, and keep coming back.*

*You can't possibly focus on your mission without also focusing on the folks that make your mission happen...since you manage* things *and lead* people, *common sense suggests that it's people who are at the core of all leadership activities.*

*Making sure that everyone knows what values are important, and then helping everyone turn those good beliefs into everyday behaviors, is how leaders create a great place to work.*

*Staying with "business as usual" probably wouldn't serve us well that much longer.*

*....involving workers in running the operation—and in making decisions that affect them—is a key strategy for leadership success.*

*As our challenges have grown with each new season, more and more I rely on teamwork, collaboration, and the contributions of each member of the workshop team. Ensuring that those things happen requires effective leadership on my part.*

*I pay attention to what my elves (and others) feel. Perceptions are realities for those who hold them...and I must deal with those realities in order to lead effectively.*

*Obviously, our job is to give people what they're looking for. And as their wants and needs change, we have to change along with them. Doing that starts with accepting the fact that the customer is truly in charge of our business....*

*The more employees understand about how the business works, the more likely they are to accept and support change.*

*Nothing motivates employees more than knowing they're making a difference.*

*I've learned that recognizing employees—doing right by those who do right—is one of the best things I can do for my elves and reindeer—and for myself as well. I feel good when I do it...they feel good when they receive it... and they're more motivated, and therefore more likely to repeat the performance I want and need in the future.*

*You see, I'm the leader here. And obviously, I have a strong influence on the thoughts and behaviors of the elves and reindeer. They rightfully assume that it's okay to do whatever I do. Regardless of what's said or written elsewhere in the workshop, my actions—whether good or bad—are the performance standards that they will follow.*

*...being good and doing right are not* sometime *things—they're* every *time things involving everything we do. EVERYTHING COUNTS—for your people, and especially for* you *as their leader.*

# THE LEADERSHIP SECRETS OF SANTA CLAUS
## SUMMARY CHECKLIST

### 1. Build a Wonderful Workshop
- ❏ Make the Mission the Main Thing
- ❏ Focus on Your People As Well As Your Purpose
- ❏ Let Values Be Your Guide

### 2. Choose Your Reindeer Wisely
- ❏ Hire Tough So You Can Manage Easy
- ❏ Promote the Right Ones..for the Right Reasons
- ❏ Go for the Diversity Advantage

### 3. Make a List and Check It Twice
- ❏ Plan Your Work
- ❏ Work Your Plan
- ❏ Make the Most of What You Have

### 4. Listen to the Elves
- ❏ Open Your Ears to Participation
- ❏ Pay Attention to How You're Perceived
- ❏ Walk Awhile in *Their* Shoes

### 5. Say Ho Ho Ho, but Don't Forget the Snow
- ❏ Build Contagious Enthusiasm
- ❏ Expect the Unexpected
- ❏ Get Problems Solved...Together

### 6. Give Them Gifts That Last a Lifetime
- ❏ Teach Success Skills
- ❏ Reinforce Relationships
- ❏ Push Pride and Professionalism

### 7. Get beyond the Red Wagons
- ❏ Help Everyone Accept the Reality of Change
- ❏ Remember: The Customer Is Really in Charge
- ❏ Teach "the Business" of the Business

### 8. Share the Milk and Cookies
- ❏ Help Them See the Difference They Make
- ❏ Do Right by Those Who Do Right
- ❏ Expand the Reinforcement Possibilities

### 9. Find Out Who's Naughty and Nice
- ❏ Confront Performance Problems...Early
- ❏ Coach "the Majority in the Middle"
- ❏ Don't Forget "the Super Stars"

### 10. Be Good for Goodness Sake
- ❏ Set the Example
- ❏ Establish Guidelines and Accountability
- ❏ Remember That Everything Counts

*Never forget that getting things done all year long isn't about magic, it's about LEADERSHIP!*

*- Santa*

# NOTES

……………………………………………………………
……………………………………………………………
……………………………………………………………
……………………………………………………………
……………………………………………………………
……………………………………………………………
……………………………………………………………
……………………………………………………………
……………………………………………………………
……………………………………………………………
……………………………………………………………
……………………………………………………………
……………………………………………………………
……………………………………………………………
……………………………………………………………
……………………………………………………………
……………………………………………………………